CW00820204

Advanced Higher

Mathematics

2003 Exam

2004 Exam

2005 Exam

2006 Exam

2007 Exam

Leckie ✕ Leckie

© Scottish Qualifications Authority
All rights reserved. Copying prohibited. No part of this publication may be reproduced, stored in a retrieval system, or transmitted
in any form or by any means, electronic, mechanical, photocopying, recording or otherwise.

First exam published in 2003.
Published by Leckie & Leckie Ltd, 3rd Floor, 4 Queen Street, Edinburgh EH2 1JE
tel: 0131 220 6831 fax: 0131 225 9987 enquiries@leckieandleckie.co.uk www.leckieandleckie.co.uk

ISBN 978-1-84372-570-1

A CIP Catalogue record for this book is available from the British Library.

Printed in Scotland by Scotprint.

Leckie & Leckie is a division of Huveaux plc.

Leckie & Leckie is grateful to the copyright holders, as credited at the back of the book, for permission to use their material.
Every effort has been made to trace the copyright holders and to obtain their permission for the use of copyright material.
Leckie & Leckie will gladly receive information enabling them to rectify any error or omission in subsequent editions.

2003 | Advanced Higher

[BLANK PAGE]

X100/701

NATIONAL QUALIFICATIONS 2003

WEDNESDAY, 21 MAY 1.00 PM – 4.00 PM

MATHEMATICS ADVANCED HIGHER

(adapted to match 2004 exam paper)

Read carefully

1. Calculators may be used in this paper.

2. Candidates should answer all questions.

3. **Full credit will be given only where the solution contains appropriate working.**

SCOTTISH
QUALIFICATIONS
AUTHORITY

Marks

Answer all the questions

1. (a)   Given $f(x) = x(1 + x)^{10}$, obtain $f'(x)$ and simplify your answer. **3**

    (b)   Given $y = 3^x$, use logarithmic differentiation to obtain $\dfrac{dy}{dx}$ in terms of x. **3**

2. Given that $u_k = 11 - 2k$, $(k \geq 1)$, obtain a formula for $S_n = \displaystyle\sum_{k=1}^{n} u_k$. **3**
    Find the values of n for which $S_n = 21$. **2**

3. The equation $y^3 + 3xy = 3x^2 - 5$ defines a curve passing through the point $A\,(2, 1)$. Obtain an equation for the tangent to the curve at A. **4**

4. Identify the locus in the complex plane given by $|z + i| = 2$. **3**

5. Use the substitution $x = 1 + \sin\theta$ to evaluate $\displaystyle\int_{0}^{\pi/2} \dfrac{\cos\theta}{(1 + \sin\theta)^3}\, d\theta$. **5**

6. Use elementary row operations to reduce the following system of equations to upper triangular form

    $$
    \begin{array}{rcrcrcr}
    x &+& y &+& 3z &=& 1 \\
    3x &+& ay &+& z &=& 1 \\
    x &+& y &+& z &=& -1.
    \end{array}
    $$
    2

    Hence express x, y and z in terms of the parameter a. **2**

    Explain what happens when $a = 3$. **2**

7.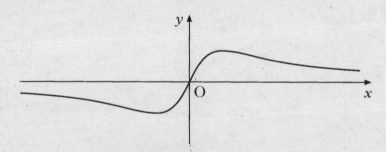

    The diagram shows the shape of the graph of $y = \dfrac{x}{1 + x^2}$. Obtain the stationary points of the graph. **4**

    Sketch the graph of $y = \left| \dfrac{x}{1 + x^2} \right|$ and identify its three critical points. **3**

Marks

8. Given that $p(n) = n^2 + n$, where n is a positive integer, consider the statements:

   A $p(n)$ is always even

   B $p(n)$ is always a multiple of 3.

   For each statement, prove it if it is true or, otherwise, disprove it.   4

9. Given that $w = \cos\theta + i\sin\theta$, show that $\frac{1}{w} = \cos\theta - i\sin\theta$.   1

   Use de Moivre's theorem to prove $w^k + w^{-k} = 2\cos k\theta$, where k is a natural number.   3

   Expand $(w + w^{-1})^4$ by the binomial theorem and hence show that

   $$\cos^4\theta = \tfrac{1}{8}\cos 4\theta + \tfrac{1}{2}\cos 2\theta + \tfrac{3}{8}.$$ 5

10. Define $I_n = \int_0^1 x^n e^{-x}dx$ for $n \geq 1$.

    (a) Use integration by parts to obtain the value of $I_1 = \int_0^1 xe^{-x}dx$.   3

    (b) Similarly, show that $I_n = nI_{n-1} - e^{-1}$ for $n \geq 2$.   4

    (c) Evaluate I_3.   3

11. The volume $V(t)$ of a cell at time t changes according to the law

    $$\frac{dV}{dt} = V(10 - V) \qquad \text{for } 0 < V < 10.$$

    Show that

    $$\tfrac{1}{10}\ln V - \tfrac{1}{10}\ln(10 - V) = t + C$$

    for some constant C.   4

    Given that $V(0) = 5$, show that

    $$V(t) = \frac{10e^{10t}}{1 + e^{10t}}.$$ 3

    Obtain the limiting value of $V(t)$ as $t \to \infty$.   2

Marks

12. Find the point of intersection of the line

$$\frac{x-3}{4} = \frac{y-2}{1} = \frac{z+1}{2}$$

and the plane with equation $2x + y - z = 4$.

4

13. The matrix A is such that $A^2 = 4A - 3I$ where I is the corresponding identity matrix. Find integers p and q such that

$$A^4 = pA + qI.$$

4

14. A recurrence relation is defined by the formula

$$x_{n+1} = \frac{1}{2}\left\{x_n + \frac{7}{x_n}\right\}.$$

Find the fixed points of this recurrence relation.

3

15. Obtain the Maclaurin series for $f(x) = \sin^2 x$ up to the term in x^4.

4

Hence write down a series for $\cos^2 x$ up to the term in x^4.

1

16. (a) Prove by induction that for all natural numbers $n \geq 1$

$$\sum_{r=1}^{n} 3(r^2 - r) = (n - 1)n(n + 1).$$

4

(b) Hence evaluate $\sum_{r=11}^{40} 3(r^2 - r)$.

2

17. Solve the differential equation

$$\frac{d^2 y}{dx^2} - 4\frac{dy}{dx} + 4y = e^x,$$

given that $y = 2$ and $\frac{dy}{dx} = 1$, when $x = 0$.

10

[END OF QUESTION PAPER]

2004 | Advanced Higher

[BLANK PAGE]

X100/701

NATIONAL
QUALIFICATIONS
2004

FRIDAY, 21 MAY
1.00 PM – 4.00 PM

MATHEMATICS
ADVANCED HIGHER

Read carefully

1. Calculators may be used in this paper.

2. Candidates should answer all questions.

3. **Full credit will be given only where the solution contains appropriate working.**

SCOTTISH
QUALIFICATIONS
AUTHORITY

Marks

Answer all the questions.

1. (a) Given $f(x) = \cos^2 x \, e^{\tan x}$, $-\frac{\pi}{2} < x < \frac{\pi}{2}$, obtain $f'(x)$ and evaluate $f'(\frac{\pi}{4})$. **3,1**

    (b) Differentiate $g(x) = \dfrac{\tan^{-1} 2x}{1 + 4x^2}$. **3**

2. Obtain the binomial expansion of $(a^2 - 3)^4$. **3**

3. A curve is defined by the equations

    $$x = 5\cos\theta, \qquad y = 5\sin\theta, \qquad (0 \le \theta < 2\pi).$$

    Use parametric differentiation to find $\dfrac{dy}{dx}$ in terms of θ. **2**

    Find the equation of the tangent to the curve at the point where $\theta = \frac{\pi}{4}$. **3**

4. Given $z = 1 + 2i$, express $z^2(z + 3)$ in the form $a + ib$. **2**

    Hence, or otherwise, verify that $1 + 2i$ is a root of the equation

    $$z^3 + 3z^2 - 5z + 25 = 0.$$ **2**

    Obtain the other roots of this equation. **2**

5. Express $\dfrac{1}{x^2 - x - 6}$ in partial fractions. **2**

    Evaluate $\displaystyle\int_0^1 \frac{1}{x^2 - x - 6}\,dx$. **4**

6. Write down the 2×2 matrix M_1 associated with an anti-clockwise rotation of $\frac{\pi}{2}$ radians about the origin. **2**

    Write down the matrix M_2 associated with reflection in the x-axis. **1**

    Evaluate $M_2 M_1$ and describe geometrically the effect of the transformation represented by $M_2 M_1$. **2**

7. Obtain the first three non-zero terms in the Maclaurin expansion of $f(x) = e^x \sin x$. **5**

8. Use the Euclidean algorithm to show that $(231, 17) = 1$ where (a, b) denotes the highest common factor of a and b.

    Hence find integers x and y such that $231x + 17y = 1$. **4**

9. Use the substitution $x = (u - 1)^2$ to obtain $\displaystyle\int \frac{1}{(1 + \sqrt{x})^3}\,dx$. **5**

Marks

10. Determine whether the function $f(x) = x^4 \sin 2x$ is odd, even or neither.

    Justify your answer.

    3

11. A solid is formed by rotating the curve $y = e^{-2x}$ between $x = 0$ and $x = 1$ through $360°$ about the x-axis. Calculate the volume of the solid that is formed.

    5

12. Prove by induction that $\dfrac{d^n}{dx^n}(xe^x) = (x + n)e^x$ for all integers $n \geq 1$.

    5

13. The function f is defined by $f(x) = \dfrac{x-3}{x+2}$, $x \neq -2$, and the diagram shows part of its graph.

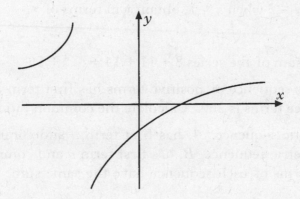

    (a) Obtain algebraically the asymptotes of the graph of f.

    3

    (b) Prove that f has no stationary values.

    2

    (c) Does the graph of f have any points of inflexion? Justify your answer.

    2

    (d) Sketch the graph of the inverse function, f^{-1}. State the asymptotes and domain of f^{-1}.

    3

14. (a) Find an equation of the plane π_1 containing the points $A(1, 0, 3)$, $B(0, 2, -1)$ and $C(1, 1, 0)$.

    4

    Calculate the size of the acute angle between π_1 and the plane π_2 with equation $x + y - z = 0$.

    3

    (b) Find the point of intersection of plane π_2 and the line

    $$\frac{x-11}{4} = \frac{y-15}{5} = \frac{z-12}{2}.$$

    3

[Turn over for Questions 15 and 16 on *Page four*

Marks

15. (a) A mathematical biologist believes that the differential equation $x\dfrac{dy}{dx} - 3y = x^4$ models a process. Find the general solution of the differential equation.

    5

    Given that $y = 2$ when $x = 1$, find the particular solution, expressing y in terms of x.

    2

    (b) The biologist subsequently decides that a better model is given by the equation $y\dfrac{dy}{dx} - 3x = x^4$.

    Given that $y = 2$ when $x = 1$, obtain y in terms of x.

    4

16. (a) Obtain the sum of the series $8 + 11 + 14 + \ldots + 56$.

    2

    (b) A geometric sequence of positive terms has first term 2, and the sum of the first three terms is 266. Calculate the common ratio.

    3

    (c) An arithmetic sequence, A, has first term a and common difference 2, and a geometric sequence, B, has first term a and common ratio 2. The first four terms of each sequence have the same sum. Obtain the value of a.

    3

    Obtain the smallest value of n such that the sum to n terms for sequence B is more than **twice** the sum to n terms for sequence A.

    2

[END OF QUESTION PAPER]

[BLANK PAGE]

X100/701

NATIONAL
QUALIFICATIONS
2005

FRIDAY, 20 MAY
1.00 PM – 4.00 PM

MATHEMATICS
ADVANCED HIGHER

Read carefully

1. Calculators may be used in this paper.

2. Candidates should answer **all** questions.

3. **Full credit will be given only where the solution contains appropriate working.**

SCOTTISH
QUALIFICATIONS
AUTHORITY

Marks

Answer all the questions.

1. (a) Given $f(x) = x^3 \tan 2x$, where $0 < x < \frac{\pi}{4}$, obtain $f'(x)$.   **3**

   (b) For $y = \frac{1 + x^2}{1 + x}$, where $x \neq -1$, determine $\frac{dy}{dx}$ in simplified form.   **3**

2. Given the equation $2y^2 - 2xy - 4y + x^2 = 0$ of a curve, obtain the x-coordinate of each point at which the curve has a horizontal tangent.   **4**

3. Write down the Maclaurin expansion of e^x as far as the term in x^4.   **2**

   Deduce the Maclaurin expansion of e^{x^2} as far as the term in x^4.   **1**

   Hence, or otherwise, find the Maclaurin expansion of $e^{x + x^2}$ as far as the term in x^4.   **3**

4. The sum, $S(n)$, of the first n terms of a sequence, $u_1, u_2, u_3, \ldots$ is given by $S(n) = 8n - n^2$, $n \geq 1$.

   Calculate the values of u_1, u_2, u_3 and state what type of sequence it is.   **3**

   Obtain a formula for u_n in terms of n, simplifying your answer.   **2**

5. Use the substitution $u = 1 + x$ to evaluate $\int_0^3 \frac{x}{\sqrt{1 + x}}\, dx$.   **5**

6. Use Gaussian elimination to solve the system of equations below when $\lambda \neq 2$:

$$\begin{aligned} x + y + 2z &= 1 \\ 2x + \lambda y + z &= 0 \\ 3x + 3y + 9z &= 5. \end{aligned}$$ **4**

   Explain what happens when $\lambda = 2$.   **2**

7. Given the matrix $A = \begin{pmatrix} 0 & 4 & 2 \\ 1 & 0 & 1 \\ -1 & -2 & -3 \end{pmatrix}$, show that $A^2 + A = kI$ for some

   constant k, where I is the 3×3 unit matrix.   **4**

   Obtain the values of p and q for which $A^{-1} = pA + qI$.   **2**

8. The equations of two planes are $x - 4y + 2z = 1$ and $x - y - z = -5$. By letting $z = t$, or otherwise, obtain parametric equations for the line of intersection of the planes.   **4**

   Show that this line lies in the plane with equation

$$x + 2y - 4z = -11.$$ **1**

Marks

9. Given the equation $z + 2i\bar{z} = 8 + 7i$, express z in the form $a + ib$.　　4

10. Prove by induction that, for all positive integers n,

$$\sum_{r=1}^{n} \frac{1}{r(r+1)(r+2)} = \frac{1}{4} - \frac{1}{2(n+1)(n+2)}.$$　　5

State the value of $\displaystyle\lim_{n\to\infty} \sum_{r=1}^{n} \frac{1}{r(r+1)(r+2)}$.　　1

11. The diagram shows part of the graph of $y = \dfrac{x^3}{x-2}$, $x \neq 2$.

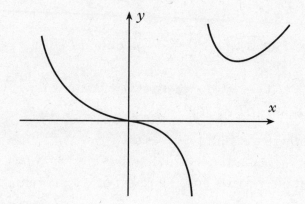

(a) Write down the equation of the vertical asymptote.　　1

(b) Find the coordinates of the stationary points of the graph of $y = \dfrac{x^3}{x-2}$.　　4

(c) Write down the coordinates of the stationary points of the graph of
$y = \left| \dfrac{x^3}{x-2} \right| + 1$.　　2

12. Let $z = \cos\theta + i\sin\theta$.

(a) Use the binomial expansion to express z^4 in the form $u + iv$, where u and v are expressions involving $\sin\theta$ and $\cos\theta$.　　3

(b) Use de Moivre's theorem to write down a second expression for z^4.　　1

(c) Using the results of (a) and (b), show that

$$\frac{\cos 4\theta}{\cos^2\theta} = p\cos^2\theta + q\sec^2\theta + r, \text{ where } -\frac{\pi}{2} < \theta < \frac{\pi}{2},$$

stating the values of p, q and r.　　6

[Turn over for Questions 13, 14 and 15 on *Page four*

Marks

13. Express $\dfrac{1}{x^3 + x}$ in partial fractions. — 4

Obtain a formula for $I(k)$, where $I(k) = \displaystyle\int_1^k \dfrac{1}{x^3 + x}\, dx$, expressing it in the form $\ln\left(\dfrac{a}{b}\right)$, where a and b depend on k. — 4

Write down an expression for $e^{I(k)}$ and obtain the value of $\displaystyle\lim_{k \to \infty} e^{I(k)}$. — 2

14. Obtain the general solution of the differential equation

$$\frac{d^2y}{dx^2} - 3\frac{dy}{dx} + 2y = 20\sin x.$$

— 7

Hence find the particular solution for which $y = 0$ and $\dfrac{dy}{dx} = 0$ when $x = 0$. — 3

15. (a) Given $f(x) = \sqrt{\sin x}$, where $0 < x < \pi$, obtain $f'(x)$. — 1

(b) If, in general, $f(x) = \sqrt{g(x)}$, where $g(x) > 0$, show that $f'(x) = \dfrac{g'(x)}{k\sqrt{g(x)}}$, stating the value of k. — 2

Hence, or otherwise, find $\displaystyle\int \dfrac{x}{\sqrt{1-x^2}}\, dx$. — 3

(c) Use integration by parts and the result of (b) to evaluate

$$\int_0^{1/2} \sin^{-1}x \, dx.$$

— 4

[END OF QUESTION PAPER]

2006 | Advanced Higher

[BLANK PAGE]

[BLANK PAGE]

X100/701

NATIONAL
QUALIFICATIONS
2006

FRIDAY, 19 MAY
1.00 PM – 4.00 PM

MATHEMATICS
ADVANCED HIGHER

Read carefully

1. Calculators may be used in this paper.

2. Candidates should answer **all** questions.

3. **Full credit will be given only where the solution contains appropriate working.**

SCOTTISH
QUALIFICATIONS
AUTHORITY

©

Marks

Answer all the questions.

1. Calculate the inverse of the matrix $\begin{pmatrix} 2 & x \\ -1 & 3 \end{pmatrix}$.

    For what value of x is this matrix singular?   **4**

2. Differentiate, simplifying your answers:

    (a) $2\tan^{-1}\sqrt{1+x}$, where $x > -1$;   **3**

    (b) $\dfrac{1+\ln x}{3x}$, where $x > 0$.   **3**

3. Express the complex number $z = -i + \dfrac{1}{1-i}$ in the form $z = x + iy$, stating the values of x and y.   **3**

    Find the modulus and argument of z and plot z and $\bar{z}$ on an Argand diagram.   **4**

4. Given $xy - x = 4$, use implicit differentiation to obtain $\dfrac{dy}{dx}$ in terms of x and y.   **2**

    Hence obtain $\dfrac{d^2y}{dx^2}$ in terms of x and y.   **3**

5. Obtain algebraically the fixed point of the iterative scheme given by

    $$x_{n+1} = \frac{1}{2}\left(x_n + \frac{2}{x_n^2}\right), \qquad n = 0, 1, 2, \ldots .$$ **3**

6. Find $\displaystyle\int \frac{12x^3 - 6x}{x^4 - x^2 + 1}\, dx$.   **3**

7. For all natural numbers n, prove whether the following results are true or false.

    (a) $n^3 - n$ is always divisible by 6.

    (b) $n^3 + n + 5$ is always prime.   **5**

8. Solve the differential equation

    $$\frac{d^2y}{dx^2} + 2\frac{dy}{dx} + 2y = 0,$$

    given that when $x = 0$, $y = 0$ and $\dfrac{dy}{dx} = 2$.   **6**

Marks

9. Use Gaussian elimination to obtain solutions of the equations

$$2x - y + 2z = 1$$
$$x + y - 2z = 2$$
$$x - 2y + 4z = -1.$$

5

10. The amount x micrograms of an impurity removed per kg of a substance by a chemical process depends on the temperature $T\,°C$ as follows:

$$x = T^3 - 90T^2 + 2400T, \qquad 10 \le T \le 60.$$

At what temperature in the given range should the process be carried out to remove as much impurity per kg as possible?

4

11. Show that $1 + \cot^2\theta = \mathrm{cosec}^2\theta$, where $0 < \theta < \dfrac{\pi}{2}$.

1

By expressing $y = \cot^{-1}x$ as $x = \cot y$, obtain $\dfrac{dy}{dx}$ in terms of x.

3

12.

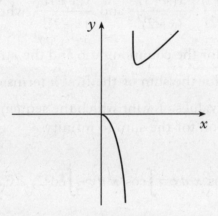

The diagram shows part of the graph of a function f which satisfies the following conditions:

(i) f is an even function;

(ii) two of the asymptotes of the graph $y = f(x)$ are $y = x$ and $x = 1$.

Copy the diagram and complete the graph. Write down equations for the other two asymptotes.

3

13. The square matrices A and B are such that $AB = BA$. Prove by induction that $A^nB = BA^n$ for all integers $n \ge 1$.

5

[Turn over for Questions 14 to 17 on *Page four*

Marks

14. (a) Determine whether $f(x) = x^2 \sin x$ is odd, even or neither. Justify your answer. **3**

(b) Use integration by parts to find $\int x^2 \sin x\, dx$. **4**

(c) Hence find the area bounded by $y = x^2 \sin x$, the lines $x = -\dfrac{\pi}{4}$, $x = \dfrac{\pi}{4}$ and the x-axis. **3**

15. Obtain an equation for the plane passing through the point $P(1, 1, 0)$ which is perpendicular to the line L given by

$$\frac{x+1}{2} = \frac{y-2}{1} = \frac{z}{-1}.$$ **3**

Find the coordinates of the point Q where the plane and L intersect. **4**

Hence, or otherwise, obtain the shortest distance from P to L and explain why this is the shortest distance. **2, 1**

16. The first three terms of a geometric sequence are

$$\frac{x(x+1)}{(x-2)},\ \frac{x(x+1)^2}{(x-2)^2}\ \text{ and }\ \frac{x(x+1)^3}{(x-2)^3},\ \text{ where } x<2.$$

(a) Obtain expressions for the common ratio and the nth term of the sequence. **3**

(b) Find an expression for the sum of the first n terms of the sequence. **3**

(c) Obtain the range of values of x for which the sequence has a sum to infinity and find an expression for the sum to infinity. **4**

17. (a) Show that $\displaystyle\int \sin^2 x \cos^2 x\, dx = \int \cos^2 x\, dx - \int \cos^4 x\, dx.$ **1**

(b) By writing $\cos^4 x = \cos x \cos^3 x$ and using integration by parts, show that

$$\int_0^{\pi/4} \cos^4 x\, dx = \frac{1}{4} + 3\int_0^{\pi/4} \sin^2 x \cos^2 x\, dx.$$ **3**

(c) Show that $\displaystyle\int_0^{\pi/4} \cos^2 x\, dx = \frac{\pi+2}{8}.$ **3**

(d) Hence, using the above results, show that

$$\int_0^{\pi/4} \cos^4 x\, dx = \frac{3\pi+8}{32}.$$ **3**

[END OF QUESTION PAPER]

[BLANK PAGE]

X100/701

| NATIONAL QUALIFICATIONS 2007 | TUESDAY, 15 MAY 1.00 PM – 4.00 PM | MATHEMATICS ADVANCED HIGHER |

Read carefully

1. Calculators may be used in this paper.

2. Candidates should answer **all** questions.

3. **Full credit will be given only where the solution contains appropriate working.**

SCOTTISH
QUALIFICATIONS
AUTHORITY

Marks

Answer all the questions.

1. Express the binomial expansion of $\left(x - \dfrac{2}{x}\right)^4$ in the form $ax^4 + bx^2 + c + \dfrac{d}{x^2} + \dfrac{e}{x^4}$

   for integers a, b, c, d and e.

   4

2. Obtain the derivative of each of the following functions:

   (a) $f(x) = \exp(\sin 2x)$; **3**

   (b) $y = 4^{(x^2 + 1)}$. **3**

3. Show that $z = 3 + 3i$ is a root of the equation $z^3 - 18z + 108 = 0$ and obtain the remaining roots of the equation.

   4

4. Express $\dfrac{2x^2 - 9x - 6}{x(x^2 - x - 6)}$ in partial fractions. **3**

   Given that

   $$\int_4^6 \frac{2x^2 - 9x - 6}{x(x^2 - x - 6)}\,dx = \ln\frac{m}{n},$$

   determine values for the integers m and n.

   3

5. Matrices A and B are defined by

   $$A = \begin{pmatrix} 1 & 0 & -1 \\ 0 & 1 & -1 \\ 0 & 1 & 2 \end{pmatrix}, \qquad B = \begin{pmatrix} x+2 & x-2 & x+3 \\ -4 & 4 & 2 \\ 2 & -2 & 3 \end{pmatrix}.$$

   (a) Find the product AB. **2**

   (b) Obtain the determinants of A and of AB. **2**

   Hence, or otherwise, obtain an expression for det B. **1**

6. Find the Maclaurin series for $\cos x$ as far as the term in x^4. **2**

   Deduce the Maclaurin series for $f(x) = \frac{1}{2}\cos 2x$ as far as the term in x^4. **2**

   Hence write down the first three non-zero terms of the series for $f(3x)$. **1**

Marks

7. Use the Euclidean algorithm to find integers p and q such that $599p + 53q = 1$. **4**

8. Obtain the general solution of the equation $\dfrac{d^2y}{dx^2} + 6\dfrac{dy}{dx} + 9y = e^{2x}$. **6**

9. Show that $\displaystyle\sum_{r=1}^{n}(4 - 6r) = n - 3n^2$. **2**

Hence write down a formula for $\displaystyle\sum_{r=1}^{2q}(4 - 6r)$. **1**

Show that $\displaystyle\sum_{r=q+1}^{2q}(4 - 6r) = q - 9q^2$. **2**

10. Use the substitution $u = 1 + x^2$ to obtain $\displaystyle\int_0^1 \dfrac{x^3}{(1+x^2)^4}\,dx$. **5**

A solid is formed by rotating the curve $y = \dfrac{x^{3/2}}{(1+x^2)^2}$ between $x = 0$ and $x = 1$

through $360°$ about the x-axis. Write down the volume of this solid. **1**

11. Given that $|z - 2| = |z + i|$, where $z = x + iy$, show that $ax + by + c = 0$ for suitable values of a, b and c. **3**

Indicate on an Argand diagram the locus of complex numbers z which satisfy $|z - 2| = |z + i|$. **1**

12. Prove by induction that for $a > 0$,

$$(1 + a)^n \geq 1 + na$$

for all positive integers n. **5**

13. A curve is defined by the parametric equations $x = \cos 2t$, $y = \sin 2t$, $0 < t < \dfrac{\pi}{2}$.

   (a) Use parametric differentiation to find $\dfrac{dy}{dx}$.

       Hence find the equation of the tangent when $t = \dfrac{\pi}{8}$. **5**

   (b) Obtain an expression for $\dfrac{d^2y}{dx^2}$ and hence show that $\sin 2t\,\dfrac{d^2y}{dx^2} + \left(\dfrac{dy}{dx}\right)^2 = k$,

       where k is an integer. State the value of k. **5**

[Turn over for Questions 14 to 16 on *Page four*

Marks

14. A garden centre advertises young plants to be used as hedging.

   After planting, the growth G metres (ie the increase in height) after t years is modelled by the differential equation

$$\frac{dG}{dt} = \frac{25k - G}{25}$$

   where k is a constant and $G = 0$ when $t = 0$.

   (a) Express G in terms of t and k.　　　　　4

   (b) Given that a plant grows 0·6 metres by the end of 5 years, find the value of k correct to 3 decimal places.　　　　　2

   (c) On the plant labels it states that the expected growth after 10 years is approximately 1 metre. Is this claim justified?　　　　　2

   (d) Given that the initial height of the plants was 0·3 m, what is the likely long-term height of the plants?　　　　　2

15. Lines L_1 and L_2 are given by the parametric equations

$$L_1 : x = 2 + s, \ y = -s, \ z = 2 - s \qquad L_2 : x = -1 - 2t, \ y = t, \ z = 2 + 3t.$$

   (a) Show that L_1 and L_2 do not intersect.　　　　　3

   (b) The line L_3 passes through the point $P(1, 1, 3)$ and its direction is perpendicular to the directions of both L_1 and L_2. Obtain parametric equations for L_3.　　　　　3

   (c) Find the coordinates of the point Q where L_3 and L_2 intersect and verify that P lies on L_1.　　　　　3

   (d) PQ is the shortest distance between the lines L_1 and L_2. Calculate PQ.　　　　　1

16.

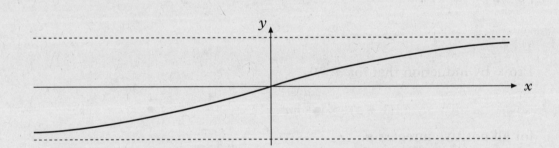

   (a) The diagram shows part of the graph of $f(x) = \tan^{-1} 2x$ and its asymptotes. State the equations of these asymptotes.　　　　　2

   (b) Use integration by parts to find the area between $f(x)$, the x-axis and the lines $x = 0$, $x = \frac{1}{2}$.　　　　　5

   (c) Sketch the graph of $y = |f(x)|$ and calculate the area between this graph, the x-axis and the lines $x = -\frac{1}{2}$, $x = \frac{1}{2}$.　　　　　3

[END OF QUESTION PAPER]

© 2007 Scottish Qualifications Authority, All Rights Reserved
Published by Leckie & Leckie Ltd, 3rd Floor, 4 Queen Street, Edinburgh EH2 1JE
tel: 0131 220 6831, fax: 0131 225 9987, enquiries@leckieandleckie.co.uk, www.leckieandleckie.co.uk

Advanced Higher Mathematics
2003

1. (a) $f'(x) = (1 + 11x)(1 + x)^9$

   (b) $\dfrac{dy}{dx} = \ln 3 \times 3^x$

2. $S_n = -n^2 + 10n$
   The sum is 21 when there are 3 terms and when there are 7 terms.

3. $x = y + 1$ (or equivalent)

4. $x^2 + (1 + y)^2 = 4$ i.e. circle centre $(0, -1)$, radius 2.

5. $\displaystyle\int_0^{\pi/2} \dfrac{\cos\theta}{(1 + \sin\theta)^3}\, d\theta = \dfrac{3}{8}$

6. $\quad x + y + 3z = 1$
   $\quad (a - 3)y - 8z = -2$
   $\qquad\qquad -2z = -2$

   $z = 1;\ y = \dfrac{6}{a - 3};\ x = -2 + \dfrac{6}{3 - a}$

   When $a = 3$, we get $z = \frac{1}{4}$ from the second equation but $z = 1$ from the third, i.e. inconsistent.

7. $y = \dfrac{x}{1 + x^2}$ has 2 stationary values: $(1, \frac{1}{2})$ and $(-1, -\frac{1}{2})$.

   $y = \left|\dfrac{x}{1 + x^2}\right|$ has two turning points: $(1, \frac{1}{2})$ and $(-1, \frac{1}{2})$
   and critical value: $(0, 0)$.

8. Statement A is true: $p(n) = n(n + 1)$ and one of n and $(n + 1)$ must be even.
   Or: n^2 and n are either both odd or both even. In either case $n^2 + n$ is even.
   Statement B is false: when $n = 1$, $n^2 + n = 2$

9. $\dfrac{1}{w} = \dfrac{1}{\cos\theta + i\sin\theta}$

   $\quad = \dfrac{1}{\cos\theta + i\sin\theta} \times \dfrac{\cos\theta - i\sin\theta}{\cos\theta - i\sin\theta}$

   $\quad = \dfrac{\cos\theta - i\sin\theta}{\cos^2\theta - i^2\sin^2\theta}$

   $\quad = \dfrac{\cos\theta - i\sin\theta}{1} = \cos\theta - i\sin\theta$

   $w^k + w^{-k} = w^k + (w^k)^{-1}$

   $\qquad = (\cos\theta + i\sin\theta)^k + \dfrac{1}{(\cos\theta + i\sin\theta)^k}$

   $\qquad = \cos k\theta + i\sin k\theta + \dfrac{1}{\cos k\theta + i\sin k\theta}$

   $\qquad = \cos k\theta + i\sin k\theta + \cos k\theta - i\sin k\theta$

   $\qquad = 2\cos k\theta$

   $(w + w^{-1})^4 = w^4 + 4w^2 + 6 + 4w^{-2} + w^{-4}$
   $(2\cos\theta)^4 = (w^4 + w^{-4}) + 4(w^2 + w^{-2}) + 6$
   $16\cos^4\theta = 2\cos 4\theta + 8\cos 2\theta + 6$

   so $\qquad \cos^4\theta = \dfrac{1}{8}\cos 4\theta + \dfrac{1}{2}\cos 2\theta + \dfrac{3}{8}$

10. (a) $I_1 = \displaystyle\int_0^1 xe^{-x}\, dx = 1 - \dfrac{2}{e} = 0.264.$

    (b) $\displaystyle\int_0^1 x^n e^{-x}\, dx = \left[x^n\int e^{-x}\, dx - \int\left(nx^{n-1}\int e^{-x}dx\right)dx\right]_0^1$

    $\qquad = [-x^n e^{-x}]_0^1 + \left[n\int x^{n-1}e^{-x}dx\right]_0^1$

    $\qquad = -e^{-1} - (-0) + n\displaystyle\int_0^1 x^{n-1}e^{-x}dx$

    $\qquad = nI_{n-1} - e^{-1}$

    (c) $I_3 = 6 - 16e^{-1} \approx 0.1139$

11.
$$\dfrac{dV}{dt} = V(10 - V)$$

$$\int \dfrac{dV}{V(10 - V)} = \int 1\, dt$$

$$\dfrac{1}{10}\int \dfrac{1}{V} + \dfrac{1}{10 - V}\, dV = \int 1\, dt$$

$$\dfrac{1}{10}(\ln V - \ln(10 - V)) = t + C$$

$$\dfrac{1}{10}\ln V - \dfrac{1}{10}\ln(10 - V) = t + C$$

$$V(0) = 5, \text{ so } \tfrac{1}{10}\ln 5 - \tfrac{1}{10}\ln 5 = 0 + C$$

$$C = 0$$

$$\ln V - \ln(10 - V) = 10t$$

$$\ln\left(\dfrac{V}{10 - V}\right) = 10t$$

$$\dfrac{V}{10 - V} = e^{10t}$$

$$V = 10e^{10t} - Ve^{10t}$$

$$V(1 + e^{10t}) = 10e^{10t}$$

$$V = \dfrac{10e^{10t}}{1 + e^{10t}}$$

$V \to 10$ as $t \to \infty$.

Advanced Higher Mathematics 2003 (cont.)

12. $(-1, 3, -3)$

13. $p = 40, q = -39$

14. The fixed points are $\sqrt{7}$ and $-\sqrt{7}$.

15. $f(x) = x^2 - \dfrac{1}{3}x^4$

$\cos^2 x = 1 - x^2 + \dfrac{1}{3}x^4$

16. (a) **Proof for $n = 1$**
LHS = 0, RHS = $0 \times 1 \times 2 = 0$.
Thus true when $n = 1$.

Inductive Hypothesis

$$\sum_{r=1}^{k} 3(r^2 - r) = (k-1)k(k+1)$$

Inductive Step

$$\sum_{r=1}^{k+1} 3(r^2 - r) = 3((k+1)^2 - (k+1)) + \sum_{r=1}^{k} 3(r^2 - r)$$

$$= 3(k+1)^2 - 3(k+1) + (k-1)k(k+1)$$
$$= (k+1)[3k + 3 - 3 + k^2 - k]$$
$$= (k+1)(k^2 + 2k)$$
$$= k(k+1)(k+2)$$
$$= ((k+1)-1)(k+1)((k+1)+1)$$

Thus true for $k + 1$. Since true for 1, true for all $n \geqslant 1$.

(b) $$\sum_{r=11}^{40} 3(r^2 - r) = 62970$$

17. General solution is $y = (A + Bx)e^{2x} + e^x$
Particular solution is $y = (1 - 2x)e^{2x} + e^x$

Advanced Higher Mathematics 2004

1. (a) $f'(x) = (1 - \sin 2x)e^{\tan x}$

$f'\left(\dfrac{\pi}{4}\right) = \left(1 - \sin\dfrac{\pi}{2}\right)e^{\tan \pi/4} = 0$

(b) $g'(x) = \dfrac{2 - 8x \tan^{-1} 2x}{(1 + 4x^2)^2}$

2. $(a^2 - 3)^4 = a^8 - 12a^6 + 54a^4 - 108a^2 + 81$

3. $\dfrac{dy}{dx} = \dfrac{5 \cos\theta}{-5 \sin\theta}$

$x + y = 5\sqrt{2}$

4. $z^2(z + 3) = -20 + 10i$
$z = 1 - 2i,\ z = -5$

5. $\dfrac{1}{x^2 - x - 6} = \dfrac{1}{5(x - 3)} - \dfrac{1}{5(x + 2)}$

$\displaystyle\int_0^1 \dfrac{1}{x^2 - x - 6}\,dx = \dfrac{1}{5}\ln\dfrac{4}{9} \approx -0 \cdot 162$

6. $M_1 = \begin{pmatrix} 0 & -1 \\ 1 & 0 \end{pmatrix},\ M_2 = \begin{pmatrix} 1 & 0 \\ 0 & -1 \end{pmatrix},\ M_2 M_1 = \begin{pmatrix} 0 & -1 \\ -1 & 0 \end{pmatrix}$

The transformation represented by $M_2 M_1$ is a reflection in $y = -x$.

7. $e^x \sin x = x + x^2 + \dfrac{1}{3}x^3$

8. $231 = 13 \times 17 + 10$
$17 = 1 \times 10 + 7$
$10 = 1 \times 7 + 3$
$7 = 2 \times 3 + 1$
Thus the highest common factor is 1.
$x = -5$ and $y = 68$

9. $\displaystyle\int \dfrac{1}{(1 + \sqrt{x})^3}\,dx = \dfrac{1}{(1 + \sqrt{x})^2} - \dfrac{2}{(1 + \sqrt{x})} + c$

10. $f(-x) = (-x)^4 \sin(-2x)$
$= -x^4 \sin 2x$
$= -f(x)$
So $f(x) = x^4 \sin 2x$ is an odd function.

11. $V = \dfrac{\pi}{4}\left[1 - \dfrac{1}{e^4}\right] \approx 0 \cdot 7706$

12. **Proof for $n = 1$**

LHS $= \dfrac{d}{dx}(xe^x) = xe^x + 1e^x = (x + 1)e^x$

RHS $= (x + 1)e^x$
So the hypothesis is true for $n = 1$.

Inductive Hypothesis

$\dfrac{d^k}{dx^k}(xe^x) = (x + k)e^x$

12. continued

Inductive Step

$$\frac{d^{k+1}}{dx^{k+1}}(xe^x) = \frac{d}{dx}\left(\frac{d^k}{dx^k}(xe^x)\right)$$

$$= \frac{d}{dx}((x+k)e^x)$$

$$= e^x + (x+k)e^x$$

$$= (x+(k+1))e^x$$

So the hypothesis being true for $n = k$ implies that it is also true for $n = k + 1$, therefore it is true for all integers $n \geqslant 1$.

13. (a) Vertical asymptote is $x = -2$
Horizontal asymptote is $y = 1$

(b) $\dfrac{dy}{dx} = \dfrac{5}{(x+2)^2} \neq 0$

(c) $\dfrac{d^2y}{dx^2} = \dfrac{-10}{(x+2)^3} \neq 0$

So there are no points of inflection.

(d)

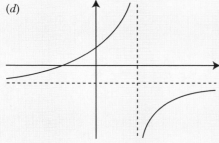

The asymptotes are $x = 1$ and $y = -2$.
The domain must exclude $x = 1$.

14. (a) $2x + 3y + z = 5$
angle $\approx 51{\cdot}9°$

(b) $(3, 5, 8)$

15. (a) $y = (x+c)x^3$; $y = (x+1)x^3$

(b) $y = \sqrt{2\left(\dfrac{x^5}{5} + \dfrac{3x^2}{5} + \dfrac{3}{10}\right)}$

16. (a) 544

(b) $r = 11$

(c) $a = \frac{12}{11}$. The smallest n is 7.

Advanced Higher Mathematics 2005

1. (a) $f(x) = x^3 \tan 2x$
$f'(x) = 3x^2 \tan 2x + x^3(2\sec^2 2x)$

(b) $y = \dfrac{1+x^2}{1+x}$

$\dfrac{dy}{dx} = \dfrac{2x(1+x) - (1+x^2).1}{(1+x)^2}$

$= \dfrac{x^2 + 2x - 1}{(1+x)^2}$

Alternative 1

$y = \dfrac{1+x^2}{1+x} = x - 1 + \dfrac{2}{1+x}$

$\dfrac{dy}{dx} = 1 - \dfrac{2}{(1+x)^2}$ or $1 - 2(1+x)^{-2}$

Alternative 2

$y = \dfrac{1+x^2}{1+x} = (1+x^2)(1+x)^{-1}$

$\dfrac{dy}{dx} = 2x(1+x)^{-1} + (1+x^2)(-1)(1+x)^2$

$\dfrac{dy}{dx} = \dfrac{2x}{(1+x)} - \dfrac{1+x^2}{(1+x)^2}$

2. $2y^2 - 2xy - 4y + x^2 = 0$

$4y\dfrac{dy}{dx} - 2x\dfrac{dy}{dx} - 2y - 4\dfrac{dy}{dx} + 2x = 0$

For a horizontal tangent

$\dfrac{dy}{dx} = 0$, so $-2y + 2x = 0$, i.e. $y = x$.

This gives $2x^2 - 2x^2 - 4x + x^2 = 0$

$\Rightarrow x(x-4) = 0$, i.e. $x = 0$ or 4.

3. $e^x = 1 + x + \dfrac{x^2}{2!} + \dfrac{x^3}{3!} + \dfrac{x^4}{4!} + ...$

$e^{x^2} = 1 + x^2 + \dfrac{x^4}{2!} + ...$

$e^{x+x^2} = e^x e^{x^2}$

$= \left(1 + x + \dfrac{x^2}{2} + \dfrac{x^3}{6} + \dfrac{x^4}{24} + ...\right)\left(1 + x^2 + \dfrac{x^4}{2} + ...\right)$

$= 1 + x + x^2 + \dfrac{x^2}{2} + \dfrac{x^3}{6} + x^3 + \dfrac{x^4}{2} + \dfrac{x^4}{2} + \dfrac{x^4}{24} + ...$

$= 1 + x + \tfrac{3}{2}x^2 + \tfrac{7}{6}x^3 + \tfrac{25}{24}x^4 + ...$

4. $u_1 = S_1 = 8 - 1 = 7$

$u_2 = S_2 - S_1 = 12 - 7 = 5$

$u_3 = S_3 - S_2 = 15 - 12 = 3$

It is an arithmetic series.
Method 1
$a = 7$ $d = -2$.
$u_n = 7 + (n-1)(-2) = 9 - 2n$.

Method 2
$u_n = S(n) - S(n-1) = 8n - n^2 - (8(n-1) - (n-1)^2)$
$= 8n - n^2 - 8n + 8 + n^2 - 2n + 1 = 9 - 2n$

Advanced Higher Mathematics
2005 (cont.)

5.
$$u = 1 + x \Rightarrow dx = du$$
When $x = 0, u = 1$ and when $x = 3, u = 4$
$$\therefore \int_0^3 \frac{x}{\sqrt{1+x}}\, dx = \int_1^4 \frac{u-1}{u^{1/2}}\, du$$
$$= \int_1^4 \left[u^{1/2} - u^{-1/2} \right] du$$
$$= \left[\frac{u^{3/2}}{3/2} - \frac{u^{1/2}}{1/2} \right]_1^4$$
$$= \left[\frac{2 \times 8}{3} - 2 \times 2 \right] - \left[\frac{2}{3} - 2 \right]$$
$$= \frac{14}{3} - 2 = 2\frac{2}{3} \ (2\cdot67 \text{ is acceptable}).$$

6.
$$\begin{pmatrix} 1 & 1 & 2 & | & 1 \\ 2 & \lambda & 1 & | & 0 \\ 3 & 3 & 9 & | & 5 \end{pmatrix} \Rightarrow \begin{pmatrix} 1 & 1 & 2 & | & 1 \\ 0 & \lambda-2 & -3 & | & -2 \\ 0 & 0 & 3 & | & 2 \end{pmatrix}$$
$$z = \tfrac{2}{3};$$
$$(\lambda - 2)y - 2 = -2 \quad y = 0; x = 1 - 0 - \tfrac{4}{3} = -\tfrac{1}{3}.$$

When $\lambda = 2$, the second and third rows of the second matrix are the same, so there is an infinite number of solutions

7.
$$A = \begin{pmatrix} 0 & 4 & 2 \\ 1 & 0 & 1 \\ -1 & -2 & -3 \end{pmatrix} \Rightarrow A^2 = \begin{pmatrix} 0 & 4 & 2 \\ 1 & 0 & 1 \\ -1 & -2 & -3 \end{pmatrix}\begin{pmatrix} 0 & 4 & 2 \\ 1 & 0 & 1 \\ -1 & -2 & -3 \end{pmatrix}$$
$$= \begin{pmatrix} 2 & -4 & -2 \\ -1 & 2 & -1 \\ 1 & 2 & 5 \end{pmatrix}$$
$$A^2 + A = \begin{pmatrix} 2 & -4 & -2 \\ -1 & 2 & -1 \\ 1 & 2 & 5 \end{pmatrix} + \begin{pmatrix} 0 & 4 & 2 \\ 1 & 0 & 1 \\ -1 & -2 & -3 \end{pmatrix}$$
$$= \begin{pmatrix} 2 & 0 & 0 \\ 0 & 2 & 0 \\ 0 & 0 & 2 \end{pmatrix} = 2I$$
$$A^{-1}(A^2 + A) = 2A^{-1}$$
$$2A^{-1} = A + I$$
$$A^{-1} = \tfrac{1}{2}A + \tfrac{1}{2}I$$

8. Using $z = t$, then
$$x - 4y = 1 - 2t$$
$$x - y = t - 5$$
Subtracting:
$$3y = 3t - 6 \Rightarrow y = t - 2$$
$$x = y + t - 5 \Rightarrow x = 2t - 7$$
The line of intersection is given by:
$$x = 2t - 7, y = t - 2, z = t.$$
$$x + 2y - 4z = 2t - 7 + 2(t-2) - 4t$$
$$= 2t - 7 + 2t - 4 - 4t = -11$$

Alternative for first 4 marks:
The normals to the planes are
$\mathbf{i} - 4\mathbf{j} + 2\mathbf{k}$ and $\mathbf{i} - \mathbf{j} - \mathbf{k}$ and the vector product of these will give the direction of the line of intersection.
$$(\mathbf{i} - 4\mathbf{j} + 2\mathbf{k}) \wedge (\mathbf{i} - \mathbf{j} - \mathbf{k}) = 6\mathbf{i} + 3\mathbf{j} + 3\mathbf{k}$$
Now obtain a point (e.g. let $z = 0$ and solve the equations $x - 4y = 1$, $x - y = -5$ gives $(-7, -2, 0)$).

Then write down the symmetric equation:
$$\frac{x+7}{6} = \frac{y+2}{3} = \frac{z}{3} = \lambda$$
which leads to $x = 6\lambda - 7, y = 3\lambda - 2, z = 3\lambda$

9. Let $z = a + ib$ so $\bar{z} = a - ib$
$$\bar{z} + 2iz = 8 + 7i$$
$$a + ib + 2ia + 2b = 8 + 7i$$
$$a + 2b = 8$$
$$2a + b = 7$$
$$3a = 6$$
$$a = 2; b = 3$$
$$z = 2 + 3i.$$

10. When $n = 1$, LHS $= \dfrac{1}{1 \times 2 \times 3} = \dfrac{1}{6}$
$$\text{RHS} = \frac{1}{4} - \frac{1}{2 \times 2 \times 3} = \frac{1}{4} - \frac{1}{12} = \frac{1}{6}.$$
Thus true for $n = 1$.
Assume true for $n = k$ and consider $n = k + 1$.
$$\sum_{r=1}^{k+1} \frac{1}{r(r+1)(r+2)}$$
$$= \sum_{r=1}^{k} \frac{1}{r(r+1)(r+2)} + \frac{1}{(k+1)(k+2)(k+3)}$$
$$= \frac{1}{4} - \frac{1}{2(k+1)(k+2)} + \frac{1}{(k+1)(k+2)(k+3)}$$
$$= \frac{1}{4} + \frac{-(k+3)+2}{2(k+1)(k+2)(k+3)}$$
$$= \frac{1}{4} - \frac{k+1}{2(k+1)(k+2)(k+3)}$$
$$= \frac{1}{4} - \frac{1}{2((k+1)+1)((k+1)+2)}$$
Hence, since true for $n = 1$, true for all positive n.
$$\lim_{n \to \infty} \sum_{r=1}^{n} \frac{1}{r(r+1)(r+2)} = \frac{1}{4}.$$

11. (a) $x = 2$

(b) $y = \dfrac{x^3}{x-2}$

$\dfrac{dy}{dx} = \dfrac{3x^2(x-2) - x^3}{(x-2)^2} = \dfrac{x^2(2x-6)}{(x-2)^2} = 0$

when $x = 0$ and when $x = 3$.

Stationary points are $(0, 0)$ and $(3, 27)$.

(c) $y = \left|\dfrac{x^3}{x-2}\right| + 1$

Stationary points are $(0, 1)$ and $(3, 28)$.

12. (a) $z^4 = (\cos\theta + i\sin\theta)^4$

$= \cos^4\theta + 4\cos^3\theta\,(i\sin\theta) + 6\cos^2\theta\,(i^2\sin^2\theta)$
$\quad + 4\cos\theta\,(i^3\sin^3\theta) + i^4\sin^4\theta$

$= \cos^4\theta + 4i\cos^3\theta\sin\theta - 6\cos^2\theta\sin^2\theta$
$\quad - 4i\cos\theta\sin^3\theta + \sin^4\theta$

$= \left(\cos^4\theta - 6\cos^2\theta\sin^2\theta + \sin^4\theta\right)$
$\quad + i\left(4\cos^3\theta\sin\theta - 4\cos\theta\sin^3\theta\right)$

(b) $(\cos\theta + i\sin\theta)^4 = \cos 4\theta + i\sin 4\theta$

(c)

Equating the real parts from (a) and (b):

$\cos 4\theta = \cos^4\theta - 6\cos^2\theta\sin^2\theta + \sin^4\theta$

$\dfrac{\cos 4\theta}{\cos^2\theta} = \cos^2\theta - 6\sin^2\theta + \sin^2\theta\dfrac{\sin^2\theta}{\cos^2\theta}$

$= \cos^2\theta - 6\left(1 - \cos^2\theta\right) + \left(1 - \cos^2\theta\right)\dfrac{1 - \cos^2\theta}{\cos^2\theta}$

$= 7\cos^2\theta - 6 + \left(\sec^2\theta - 2 + \cos^2\theta\right)$

$= 8\cos^2\theta + \sec^2\theta - 8$

$p = 8$, $q = 1$, $r = -8$.

13.

$\dfrac{1}{x^3 + x} = \dfrac{A}{x} + \dfrac{Bx + C}{x^2 + 1}$

$1 = A\left(x^2 + 1\right) + (Bx + C)x$

$x = 0 \Rightarrow 1 = A \Rightarrow A = 1$

$x = 1 \Rightarrow 1 = 2 + B + C$

$x = -1 \Rightarrow 1 = 2 + B - C$

$\Rightarrow C = 0,\ B = -1$

$\dfrac{1}{x^3 + x} = \dfrac{1}{x} - \dfrac{x}{x^2 + 1}$

$I(k) = \displaystyle\int_1^k \dfrac{1}{x^3 + x}\,dx = \int_1^k\left(\dfrac{1}{x} - \dfrac{x}{x^2 + 1}\right)dx$

$= \displaystyle\int_1^k \dfrac{1}{x}\,dx - \dfrac{1}{2}\int_1^k \dfrac{2x}{x^2 + 1}\,dx$

$= \left[\ln x\right]_1^k - \dfrac{1}{2}\left[\ln\left(x^2 + 1\right)\right]_1^k$

$= \left[\ln k - 0\right] - \dfrac{1}{2}\left[\ln\left(k^2 + 1\right) - \ln 2\right]$

$= \ln k - \ln\sqrt{k^2 + 1} + \tfrac{1}{2}\ln 2$

$= \ln\dfrac{k\sqrt{2}}{\sqrt{k^2 + 1}}$

$e^{I(k)} = \dfrac{k\sqrt{2}}{\sqrt{k^2 + 1}}$

$= \dfrac{\sqrt{2}}{\sqrt{1 + k^{-2}}} \to \sqrt{2}$

14. Let $y = e^{mx}$, then the auxiliary equation is

$m^2 - 3m + 2 = 0$

$(m - 1)(m - 2) = 0$

$m = 1 \text{ or } m = 2$

The Complementary Function is $y = Ae^x + Be^{2x}$.

For the Particular Integral, try $y = a\sin x + b\cos x$.

$\dfrac{dy}{dx} = a\cos x - b\sin x$

$\dfrac{d^2y}{dx^2} = -a\sin x - b\cos x$

Substituting:

$(-a\sin x - b\cos x) - 3(a\cos x - b\sin x)$
$\qquad\qquad + 2(a\sin x + b\cos x) = 20\sin x$

$(-a + 3b + 2a)\sin x + (-b - 3a + 2b)\cos x = 20\sin x$

$a + 3b = 20; \qquad -3a + b = 0$

$a = 2; \quad b = 6.$

The general solution is

$y = Ae^x + Be^{2x} + 2\sin x + 6\cos x$

$\dfrac{dy}{dx} = Ae^x + 2Be^{2x} + 2\cos x - 6\sin x$

$y = 0$ when $x = 0$ so $A + B + 6 = 0$.

$\frac{dy}{dx} = 0$ when $x = 0$ so $A + 2B + 2 = 0$.

$B = 4; \qquad A = -10$

The particular solution is

$y = -10e^x + 4e^{2x} + 2\sin x + 6\cos x.$

15. (a) $f(x) = (\sin x)^{1/2} \Rightarrow f'(x) = \dfrac{1}{2}\dfrac{\cos x}{(\sin x)^{1/2}}$

(b) $f(x) = \sqrt{g(x)} = [g(x)]^{1/2}$. Thus

$f'(x) = \dfrac{1}{2}g'(x)[g(x)]^{-1/2} = \dfrac{g'(x)}{2\sqrt{g(x)}}$ i.e. $k = 2$

$\displaystyle\int \dfrac{x}{\sqrt{1 - x^2}}\,dx = -\int \dfrac{-2x}{2\sqrt{1 - x^2}}\,dx$

$= -\sqrt{1 - x^2} + c$

Alternative methods for working out $\int \frac{x}{\sqrt{1-x^2}}\,dx$ include use of substitutions. For example $u = 1 - x^2$; $u^2 = 1 - x^2$; $x = \sin\theta$.

(c)

$\displaystyle\int_0^{1/2} \sin^{-1}x\,dx = \left[\sin^{-1}x\int 1.dx - \int x\dfrac{d}{dx}\left(\sin^{-1}x\right)dx\right]_0^{1/2}$

$= \left[x\sin^{-1}x - \int \dfrac{x}{\sqrt{1 - x^2}}dx\right]_0^{1/2}$

$= \left[x\sin^{-1}x + \sqrt{1 - x^2}\right]_0^{1/2}$

$= \dfrac{1}{2}\sin^{-1}\left(\dfrac{1}{2}\right) + \sqrt{\dfrac{3}{4}} - (0 + 1)$

$= \dfrac{1}{2}\dfrac{\pi}{6} + \dfrac{\sqrt{3}}{2} - 1 = \dfrac{\pi}{12} + \dfrac{\sqrt{3}}{2} - 1$

Advanced Higher Mathematics 2006

1. Let $A = \begin{pmatrix} 2 & x \\ -1 & 3 \end{pmatrix}$.

$\det A = 6 + x$

$$A^{-1} = \frac{1}{6+x}\begin{pmatrix} 3 & -x \\ 1 & 2 \end{pmatrix}$$

The matrix is singular when $x = -6$.

2. (a) $f(x) = 2\tan^{-1}\sqrt{1+x}$

$$f'(x) = \frac{2\frac{d}{dx}\left((1+x)^{1/2}\right)}{1+(1+x)}$$

$$= \frac{1}{(2+x)\sqrt{1+x}}$$

  (b) $y = \dfrac{1+\ln x}{3x}$

$$\frac{dy}{dx} = \frac{\frac{1}{x}3x - (1+\ln x)\,3}{9x^2}$$

$$= \frac{-\ln x}{3x^2}$$

3. $z = -i + \dfrac{1}{1-i} = -i + \dfrac{1}{1-i} \times \dfrac{1+i}{1+i}$

$$= -i + \frac{1+i}{2}$$

$$= \frac{1}{2} - \frac{1}{2}i$$

i.e. $x = \dfrac{1}{2}$ and $y = -\dfrac{1}{2}$

$|z| = \sqrt{\frac{1}{2}^2 + (-\frac{1}{2})^2} = \frac{1}{2}\sqrt{2}$

$\arg z = \tan^{-1}\left(\frac{-\frac{1}{2}}{\frac{1}{2}}\right) = \dfrac{-\pi}{4} \ \left(\text{or } \dfrac{7\pi}{4}\right)$

4. $xy - x = 4$

$$\frac{d}{dx}(xy) - 1 = 0$$

$$x\frac{dy}{dx} + y - 1 = 0$$

$$\frac{dy}{dx} = \frac{1-y}{x}$$

$$\frac{d^2y}{dx^2} = \frac{d}{dx}\left(\frac{1-y}{x}\right)$$

$$= \frac{-x\frac{dy}{dx} - (1-y)}{x^2}$$

$$= \frac{-x\left(\frac{1-y}{x}\right) - (1-y)}{x^2}$$

$$= \frac{2(y-1)}{x^2}$$

5. Let the fixed point be λ, then

$$\lambda = \frac{1}{2}\left(\lambda + \frac{2}{\lambda^2}\right)$$

$$\frac{\lambda}{2} = \frac{1}{\lambda^2}$$

$$\lambda^3 = 2$$

$$\lambda = \sqrt[3]{2}$$

6. $\dfrac{d}{dx}(x^4 - x^2 + 1) = 4x^3 - 2x$

Thus

$$\int \frac{12x^3 - 6x}{x^4 - x^2 + 1}\,dx = 3\int \frac{4x^3 - 2x}{x^4 - x^2 + 1}\,dx$$

$$= 3\ln(x^4 - x^2 + 1) + c$$

7. (a) $n^3 - n = n(n^2 - 1) = (n-1)n(n+1)$
Since $n^3 - n$ is the product of 3 consecutive integers, it is divisible by 3 and also by 2 so it is divisible by 6.

  (b)   Taking $n = 2$, $n^3 + n + 5 = 15$.
[Or, $n = 5$, $n^3 + n + 5 = 125 + 5 + 5$ and is divisible by 5.]
The statement is false.

8. $\dfrac{d^2y}{dx^2} + 2\dfrac{dy}{dx} + 2y = 0$

A.E. $m^2 + 2m + 2 = 0$

$$m = \frac{-2 \pm \sqrt{4-8}}{2} = -1 \pm i$$

General solution is

$$y = e^{-x}(A\cos x + B\sin x)$$

$$y = 0 \text{ when } x = 0 \Rightarrow 0 = A$$

$$\frac{dy}{dx} = -e^{-x}B\sin x + e^{-x}B\cos x$$

$$2 = 0 + B$$

The solution is $y = 2e^{-x}\sin x$.

9.

$$\begin{array}{ccc|c} 2 & -1 & 2 & 1 \\ 1 & 1 & -2 & 2 \\ 1 & -2 & 4 & -1 \end{array} \Rightarrow \begin{array}{ccc|c} 2 & -1 & 2 & 1 \\ 0 & -3 & 6 & -3 \\ 0 & 3 & -6 & 3 \end{array}$$

$$\Rightarrow \begin{array}{ccc|c} 2 & -1 & 2 & 1 \\ 0 & -3 & -6 & -3 \\ 0 & 0 & 0 & 0 \end{array}$$

Thus $z = t$, $y = 1 + 2t$ and $x = 1$.

10. $x = T^3 - 90T^2 + 2400T$

$$\frac{dx}{dT} = 3T^2 - 180T + 2400$$

$\qquad = 0$ at stationary values.

$$3(T - 40)(T - 20) = 0$$

i.e. $T = 20$ or $T = 40$

$$\frac{d^2x}{dT^2} = 6T - 180$$

$\Rightarrow T = 20$ is a local maximum
(and $T = 40$ is a local minimum).
$x(20) = 20000$

Check end of interval values

$$x(10) = 1000 - 9000 + 24000 = 16000$$
$$x(60) = 216000 - 324000 + 144000 = 36000$$

So the best result is when $T = 60$.

11. $1 + \cot^2\theta = \dfrac{\sin^2\theta + \cos^2\theta}{\sin^2\theta} = \dfrac{1}{\sin^2\theta} = \csc^2\theta$

$$y = \cot^{-1}x$$
$$\cot y = x$$
$$-\csc^2 y \frac{dy}{dx} = 1$$
$$-(1 + \cot^2 y)\frac{dy}{dx} = 1$$
$$\frac{dy}{dx} = -\frac{1}{1 + \cot^2 y}$$
$$= -\frac{1}{1 + x^2}$$

12.

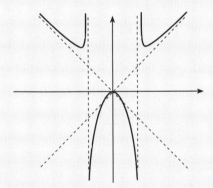

[*Asymptotes not required on the diagram.*]
The other asymptotes are $y = -x$ and $x = -1$.

13. For $n = 1$, LHS $= AB$ and RHS $= BA$. These are
equal, so true for $n = 1$.
Assume true for $n = k$, i.e. $A^kB = BA^k$.
Consider $n = k + 1$.

$$\begin{aligned}
\text{LHS} = A^{k+1}B &= A^kAB \\
&= A^kBA \\
&= BA^kA \\
&= BA^{k+1} = \text{RHS}
\end{aligned}$$

Thus if true for $n = k$, true for $n = k + 1$ and hence
true for all $n \geq 1$.

14. (a) $f(-x) = (-x)^2 \sin(-x)$
$\qquad\qquad = x^2(-\sin x) = -x^2 \sin x = -f(x)$
$\qquad$ i.e. $f(x)$ is odd

(b) $\int x^2 \sin x \, dx = x^2 \int \sin x \, dx - \int\left(2x \int \sin x \, dx\right)dx$

$\qquad = x^2(-\cos x) - \int -2x \cos x \, dx$

$\qquad = -x^2 \cos x + \left(2x\int \cos x \, dx - \int 2 \sin x \, dx\right)$

$\qquad = -x^2 \cos x + 2x \sin x + 2 \cos x + c$

(c) Since $f(x)$ is odd and the x limits are
symmetrical, the area is given by

$2\int_0^{\pi/4} f(x)dx = 2[-x^2 \cos x + 2x \sin x + 2\cos x]_0^{\pi/4}$

$= 2\left\{\left[-\left(\frac{\pi}{4}\right)^2 \cos\frac{\pi}{4} + \frac{2\pi}{4}\sin\frac{\pi}{4} + 2\cos\frac{\pi}{4}\right] - [0 + 0 + 2]\right\}$

$= 2\left(\frac{\pi}{2\sqrt{2}} + \sqrt{2} - \frac{\pi^2}{16\sqrt{2}} - 2\right)$

$= \frac{1}{8\sqrt{2}}(8\pi - \pi^2 + 32 - 32\sqrt{2})$

15. The line $\dfrac{x+1}{2} = \dfrac{y-2}{1} = \dfrac{z}{-1}$ has direction $2\mathbf{i} + \mathbf{j} - \mathbf{k}$.

An equation of the plane is $2x + y - z = k$.
Using $(1,1,0)$, $k = 2 + 1 = 3$.
i.e. $\qquad\qquad\qquad 2x + y - z = 3$.

$\qquad\qquad$ Put $\dfrac{x+1}{2} = \dfrac{y-2}{1} = \dfrac{z}{-1} = t$

$\qquad\qquad$ Hence $x = -1 + 2t$; $y = 2 + t$; $z = -t$.

$\qquad\qquad\qquad$ Substitute into $2x + y - z = 3$

$\qquad\qquad 2(-1 + 2t) + (2 + t) + t = 3$

$\qquad\qquad\qquad\qquad 6t = 3 \Rightarrow t = \frac{1}{2}$

The point of intersection, Q, is $(0, 2\frac{1}{2}, -\frac{1}{2})$
The shortest distance is PQ.

i.e. $\sqrt{1^2 + \left(\frac{3}{2}\right)^2 + \left(\frac{-1}{2}\right)^2} = \sqrt{1 + \frac{9}{4} + \frac{1}{4}} = \sqrt{\frac{7}{2}} \approx 1.87$.

This is the shortest distance because PQ is
perpendicular to L.

16. (a) $r = \dfrac{\frac{x(x+1)^2}{(x-2)^2}}{\frac{x(x+1)}{(x-2)}} = \dfrac{(x+1)}{(x-2)}$

$\qquad u_n = ar^{n-1}$

$\qquad\quad = \dfrac{x(x+1)^n}{(x-2)^n}$

(b) $S_n = \dfrac{a(r^n - 1)}{r - 1}$

$\qquad = \dfrac{x(x+1)\left(\frac{(x+1)^n}{(x-2)^n} - 1\right)}{(x-2)\left(\frac{x+1}{x-2} - 1\right)}$

$\qquad = \dfrac{1}{3}x(x+1)\left(\dfrac{(x+1)^n}{(x-2)^n} - 1\right)$

Advanced Higher Mathematics 2006 (cont.)

16. continued

(c) For a sum to infinity, $-1 < r < 1$, i.e. $r^2 < 1$

$$\frac{(x+1)^2}{(x-2)^2} < 1$$

$$x^2 + 2x + 1 < x^2 - 4x + 4$$

$$6x < 3$$

i.e. $x < \dfrac{1}{2}$

$$S = \frac{a}{1-r} = \frac{x(x+1)}{(x-2)\left(1 - \frac{x+1}{x-2}\right)}$$

$$= \frac{-x(x+1)}{3}$$

17. (a) $\int \cos^2 x \sin^2 x \, dx = \int \cos^2 x \, (1 - \cos^2 x) \, dx$
$= \int \cos^2 x \, dx - \int \cos^4 x \, dx$

(b) $\int_0^{\pi/4} \cos^4 x \, dx = \int_0^{\pi/4} \cos x \cos^3 x \, dx$

$= \left[\cos^3 x \int \cos x \, dx\right]_0^{\pi/4} - \int_0^{\pi/4} \left[3\cos^2 x \, (-\sin x) \sin x\right] dx$

$= \left[\cos^3 x \sin x\right]_0^{\pi/4} + 3\int_0^{\pi/4} \cos^2 x \sin^2 x \, dx$

$= \left(\frac{1}{\sqrt{2}}\right)^3 \frac{1}{\sqrt{2}} + 3\int_0^{\pi/4} \cos^2 x \sin^2 x \, dx$

$= \frac{1}{4} + 3\int_0^{\pi/4} \cos^2 x \sin^2 x \, dx$

(c) From $\cos 2x = 2\cos^2 x - 1$,

we get $\cos^2 x = \frac{1}{2}(1 + \cos 2x)$

$\int_0^{\pi/4} \cos^2 x \, dx = \int_0^{\pi/4} \frac{1}{2}(1 + \cos 2x) dx$

$= \frac{1}{2}\left[x + \frac{1}{2}\sin 2x\right]_0^{\pi/4}$

$= \frac{1}{2}\left[\frac{\pi}{4} + \frac{1}{2}\right] - \frac{1}{2}[0]$

$= \frac{\pi + 2}{8}$

(d)

$\int_0^{\pi/4} \cos^4 x \, dx = \frac{1}{4} + 3\int_0^{\pi/4} \cos^2 x \sin^2 x \, dx$

$= \frac{1}{4} + 3\int_0^{\pi/4} \cos^2 x \, dx - 3\int_0^{\pi/4} \cos^4 x \, dx$

$4\int_0^{\pi/4} \cos^4 x \, dx = \frac{1}{4} + 3\left(\frac{\pi + 2}{8}\right) = \frac{3\pi + 8}{8}$

$\int_0^{\pi/4} \cos^4 x \, dx = \frac{3\pi + 8}{32}$

Advanced Higher Mathematics 2007

1. $x^4 - 8x^2 + 24 - \dfrac{32}{x^2} + \dfrac{16}{x^4}$

2. (a) $f'(x) = 2\cos 2x \exp(\sin 2x)$

(b) $\dfrac{dy}{dx} = 2x \ln 4 . 4^{(x^2+1)}$

3. $(3 + 3i)^3 = 27 + 81i + 81i^2 + 27i^3 = -54 + 54i$.
Thus $(3 + 3i)^3 - 18(3 + 3i) + 108 =$
$\qquad -54 + 54i - 54 - 54i + 108 = 0$
Since $3 + 3i$ is a root, $3 - 3i$ is a root.
These give a factor $(z - (3 + 3i))(z - (3 - 3i))$
$= (z - 3)^2 + 9 = z^2 - 6z + 18$
$z^3 - 18z + 108 = (z^2 - 6z + 18)(z + 6)$
The remaining roots are $3 - 3i$ and -6.

4. $\dfrac{2x^2 - 9x - 6}{x(x^2 - x - 6)} = \dfrac{1}{x} + \dfrac{2}{x + 2} - \dfrac{1}{x - 3}$

$\int_4^6 \dfrac{2x^2 - 9x - 6}{x(x^2 - x - 6)} dx = \ln \dfrac{8}{9}$

i.e. $m = 8$, $n = 9$

5. (a) $AB = \begin{pmatrix} x & x & x \\ -6 & 6 & -1 \\ 0 & 0 & 8 \end{pmatrix}$

(b) $\det A = 3$
$\det AB = 96x$
$\det B = 32x$

6. $\cos x = 1 - \dfrac{x^2}{2} + \dfrac{x^4}{24} - \dots$

$f(x) = \dfrac{1}{2} - x^2 + \dfrac{x^4}{3} - \dots$

$f(3x) = \dfrac{1}{2} - 9x^2 + 27x^4 - \dots$

7. $p = 10$
$q = -113$

8. $y = (A + Bx)e^{-3x} + \dfrac{1}{25}e^{2x}$

9.

$$\sum_{r=1}^{n}(4-6r) = 4\sum_{r=1}^{n} - 6\sum_{r=1}^{n}r$$

$$= 4n - 3n(n+1)$$

$$= n - 3n^2$$

$$\sum_{r=1}^{2q}(4-6r) = 2q - 12q^2$$

$$\sum_{r=q+1}^{2q}(4-6r) = \sum_{r=1}^{2q}(4-6r) - \sum_{r=1}^{q}(4-6r)$$

$$= (2q - 12q^2) - (q - 3q^2)$$

$$= q - 9q^2$$

Alternatively, an Arithmetic Series could be used for the first part:

$$a = -2, \ d = -6 \Rightarrow S_n = \tfrac{n}{2}\{2(-2) + (n-1)(-6)\}$$
$$= -2n - 3n^2 + 3n$$
$$= n - 3n^2$$

10. $1 + x^2 = u \Rightarrow 2x\,dx = u$

$x = 0 \Rightarrow u = 1; \quad x = 1 \Rightarrow u = 2$

$$\int_0^1 \frac{x^3}{(1+x^2)^4}\,dx$$

$$= \int_1^2 \frac{(u-1)}{2u^4}\,du$$

$$= \frac{1}{2}\int_1^2 \left(u^{-3} - u^{-4}\right)du$$

$$= \frac{1}{2}\left[-\frac{1}{2}u^{-2} + \frac{1}{3}u^{-3}\right]_1^2$$

$$= \frac{1}{24}$$

Hence volume of revolution $= \dfrac{\pi}{24}$

11.

$$|z - 2| = |z + i|$$
$$|(x-2) + iy| = |x + (y+1)i|$$
$$(x-2)^2 + y^2 = x^2 + (y+1)^2$$
$$-4x + 4 = 2y + 1$$
$$4x + 2y - 3 = 0$$

12. Consider $n = 1$:

LHS $= (1 + a)$, RHS $= 1 + a$, so true for $n = 1$.

$$(1 + a)^{k+1} = (1 + a)(1 + a)^k$$
$$\geq (1 + a)(1 + ka)$$
$$= 1 + a + ka + ka^2$$
$$= 1 + (k+1)a + ka^2$$
$$> 1 + (k+1)a, \text{ because } ka^2 > 0$$

as required. So since true for $n = 1$, by mathematical induction, statement is true for all $n > 1$.

13. (a) $\dfrac{dy}{dx} = \dfrac{2\cos 2t}{-2\sin 2t} = -\cot 2t$

$x + y = \sqrt{2}$

(b)
$$\frac{d^2y}{dx^2} = \frac{\frac{d}{dt}\left(\frac{dy}{dx}\right)}{\frac{dx}{dt}}$$

$$= \frac{2\,\mathrm{cosec}^2\,2t}{-2\sin 2t}$$

$$= \frac{-1}{\sin^3 2t}$$

Hence:

$$\sin 2t\frac{d^2y}{dx^2} + \left(\frac{dy}{dx}\right)^2 = \frac{-\sin 2t}{\sin^3 2t} + \left(\frac{-\cos 2t}{\sin 2t}\right)^2$$

$$= \frac{-1 + \cos^2 2t}{\sin^2 2t} = -1$$

Alternatively

$$\sin 2t\frac{d^2y}{dx^2} + \left(\frac{dy}{dx}\right)^2$$

$$= -\mathrm{cosec}^2\,2t + \left(\frac{-\cos 2t}{\sin 2t}\right)^2$$

$$= \frac{-1}{\sin^2 2t} + \frac{\cos^2 2t}{\sin^2 2t}$$

$$= \frac{-1 + \cos^2 2t}{\sin^2 2t} = -1$$

14. (a) $G = 25k(1 - e^{-t/25})$

(b) $k \approx 0\cdot132$

(c) When $t = 10$, $G \approx 1\cdot09$, so claim appears to be justified.

(d) As $t \to \infty$, $G \to 25k \approx 3\cdot3$ metres, so limit is $3\cdot6$ metres.

Advanced Higher Mathematics
2007 (cont.)

15. (a) Equating the x-coordinates:

$2 + s = -1 - 2t \Rightarrow s + 2t = -3$ (1)

Equating the y-coordinates:

$-s = t \Rightarrow s = -t$

Substituting into (1):

$-t + 2t = -3 \Rightarrow t = -3 \Rightarrow s = 3$

Putting $s = 3$ in L_1 gives $(5, -3, -1)$

and $t = -3$ in L_2, $(5, -3, -7)$

As the z-coordinates differ, L_1 and L_2 do not intersect.

(b) L_3 is given by $x = 1 - 2u$, $y = 1 - u$, $z = 3 - u$

(c) The point of intersection, Q, is $(-1, 0, 2)$ since $2 + 3t = 2$ and $3 - u = 2$.

L_1 is $x = 2 + s$, $y = -s$, $z = 2 - s$.

When $x = 1$, $s = -1$ and hence $y = 1$ and $z = 3$, i.e. P lies on L_1.

(d) $PQ = \sqrt{6}$

16. (a) $\tan^{-1} 2x$ has horizontal asymptotes at $y = \pm\dfrac{\pi}{2}$.

(b) Area

$= \displaystyle\int_0^{1/2} \tan^{-1} 2x \, dx$

$= \displaystyle\int_0^{1/2} \left(\tan^{-1} 2x\right) \times 1 \, dx$

$= \left[\tan^{-1} 2x \displaystyle\int 1.dx - \displaystyle\int \dfrac{2}{1 + 4x^2} \cdot x \, dx \right]_0^{1/2}$

$= \left[x \tan^{-1} 2x - \dfrac{1}{4} \displaystyle\int \dfrac{8x}{1 + 4x^2} \, dx \right]_0^{1/2}$

$= \left[x \tan^{-1} 2x - \dfrac{1}{4} \ln\left(1 + 4x^2\right) \right]_0^{1/2}$

$= \left[\dfrac{1}{2} \tan^{-1} 1 - \dfrac{1}{4} \ln 2 \right] - \left[0 - 0 \right]$

$= \dfrac{\pi}{8} - \dfrac{1}{4} \ln 2$

(c)

$\displaystyle\int_{-1/2}^{1/2} |f(x)| \, dx = 2 \displaystyle\int_0^{1/2} \tan^{-1} 2x \, dx$

$\qquad\qquad\qquad = \dfrac{\pi}{4} - \dfrac{1}{2} \ln 2$

Official SQA answers to 978-1-84372-570-1
2003–2007